Girls'

6000

stickers

Puzzly, pretty, cutesy, and doodly!

PaRragon

Bath · New York · Cologne · Melbourne · Delhi
Hong Kong · Shenzhen · Singapore · Amsterdam

Kittens!

Which little kitten has unraveled the knitting?

A

B

C

D

How to draw a kitten ...

1

2

3

Match each kitten with its bed.

Fluff Balls

Just like this one!

Turn these cuddly balls into cats and kittens!

Kitty Fact:
Kittens begin dreaming when they are just over 1 week old!

Add your own beautiful charms to these bracelets.

Then color them all
in pretty colors!

It's **busy** at this horse riding school!

Use your stickers to show what the
horses and their riders are doing.

Splash!

These mermaids love spending lazy summer afternoons at the enchanted lagoon.

Can you find eight differences between these two pictures?

Color a shell as you find each one.

Fishy Faces

Create some little ocean creatures by adding faces to these shapes.

Mermaid Mirrors

Every mermaid needs a beautiful mirror.

Draw beautiful mermaid faces in the mirrors.

Color the mirrors with your brightest pens. You could add shiny paper, sequins, or glitter to make them shimmer in the sunlight.

Ice-Cream Cones

YUM! Doodle a big ice-cream in this glass and decorate it with swirly toppings and sweet sprinkles.

Draw some scoops of ice cream
on these ice-cream cones.

Who Lives Here?

Use your stickers to add more
furniture and the dolls to this house.

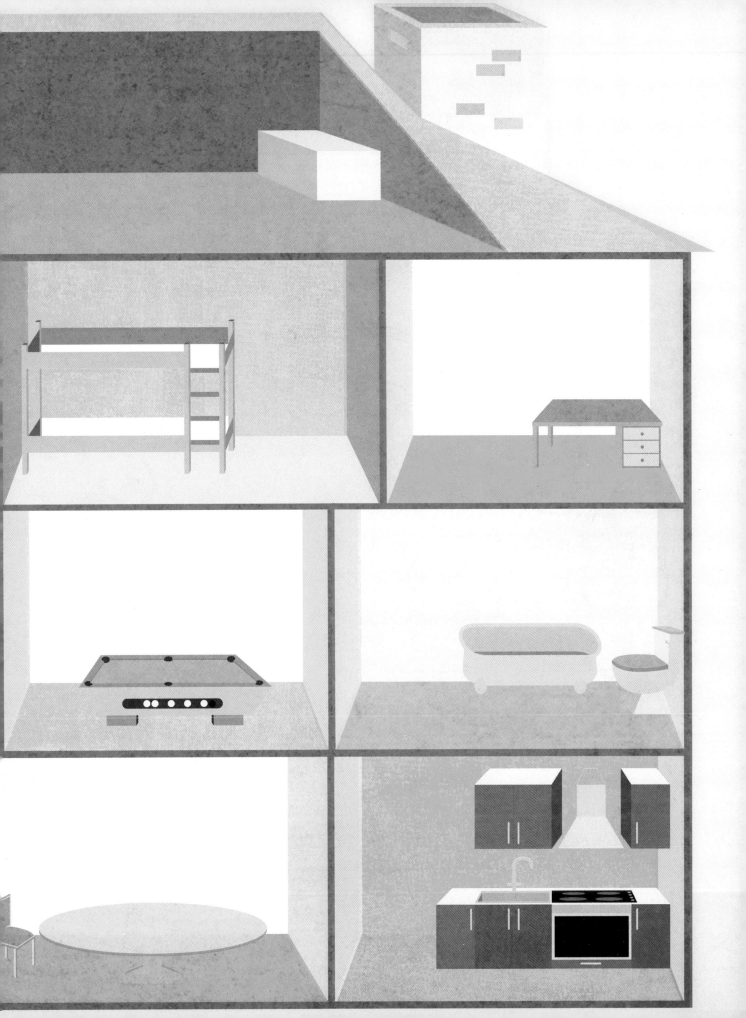

Perfect Princess

Belle of the Ball

Princess Polly is going to a Summer Ball at the Prince's palace tonight.

Help her choose shoes, a tiara, jewels, and a handbag, then color in the dress to match.

Princess Slumbers

How many mattresses does the princess have on her bed?

Princess Poppy is late for the ball! Which route will take her to her carriage and horses?

A

B

C

The Frog Prince

Princess Isabella must kiss one of these frogs in the palace pond to turn it into a handsome prince.

But which frog should she kiss?

Fill the sky with
hot air balloons.

Up, up, and away!

It's
party
time!

Use your stickers to show everyone having fun at this birthday party—don't forget to add lots of yummy treats!

Ponies!

Draw a circle around each thing Hattie needs to go horse back riding.

Saddle Up!

Penny's pony doesn't like the water jumps!
Can you show Penny a way through the show jumping
course that avoids all the water jumps?

Color in these cute ponies.
Give them each a beautiful mane and a special name.

Pretty JOSIE

Pretty Catboy

Spot five differences between these two show jumping horses.
Color a rosette for each one that you find. When you have
found them all, color the winner's trophy!

Funny Faces

Finish off these faces so they all look different.

Draw a big smile on this one.

YAWN!
Make this one
look sleepy.

The stage is set ...
now add the ballet dancers putting on a magical show!

It's a Dog's Life

Draw lines to match each poodle to its shadow.

This cute puppy is lost.
Help him find his way home
through the maze.

Love Hearts

Joselynn

Color in these cute hearts then doodle lots of your own!

Looking fabulous!

Use your stickers to add the stylish outfits these catwalk models are wearing.

Cloudy Picture

Pack the Picnic!

Circle all the things that need to be packed into the picnic basket.

Fluttering Butterflies

Color in the patterns on these butterflies.
Can you find the matching pair?

Flowers

Draw some more flowers in the park, and add some bugs crawling and flying around them.

Add wings, feelers, faces, and legs to these fingerprint bugs!

Fun at the Fair!

Use your stickers to show all the people
busy enjoying themselves at the fairground.

Double Trouble

Can you find three differences between these twins?

Color a box for each one you find.

1 2 3

Now, decorate their outfits!

Did you know?
Animals (including cats, dogs, and sheep) can be twins, too!

Summer Time!

Draw two more flowers in these pots and color them in.

Can you see three butterflies in the garden?

Trace the outline to draw the bird's house.

Swoosh! Splash! Quack!
This animal sanctuary is
packed with animals!

Use your stickers to show all the mischief and mayhem they are causing!

Magic Fairies!

Help this fairy through the forest to find her friend.

Start

Finish

How many fairies have
a wand with a star on?

Which two
of these fairies have
the same pattern on
their wings?

Dog Show

There are all kinds
of canine capers
at this dog show!

Use your stickers to show
what the dogs are doing.

Magical Mall

Fill the mall with flutterific fairies and each shop with fairy-tastic things to buy.

Fairy Wings 'R' Us

Cool!

Wand Wonders

Fairy Fashion

Fairy Furniture

Wow!

Flutter Bargains

SALE

Happy Feet

1/2 price shoes!

What will you sell?
Create a new boutique and give it a name!

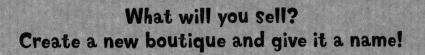

Grand opening today!

Fairy Florists

Sweet Tooth

Cute Cuts

Miss Airy Fairy

Shop till you drop!

Fluttery Friends

These fairies have decorated their wings with pretty patterns. Draw lines between the matching pairs.

FAIRY FACT:
Butterflies can't fly in the cold. They have to warm up their wings in the sun!

Fairy Good Work!

Draw Fairy Land's most sparkly resident—Princess Glitter!

1. Add butterfly-shaped wings.

2. Give the fairy princess a magic wand.

3. Make her sparkly with pretty colors and a sprinkling of stars.

Grab your best pencil and give it a try.

Pixie Park

The sun is shining, and everyone is having fun at the park. Add fairies feeding the ducks, playing on the swings, and more!

Sparkle, Twinkle Shine!

Color the jewels and add stickers to fill the box with dazzling gems.

Mirror, mirror, on the wall, who' the fairy-est of them all? Spot and circle 5 differences between Snowflake and her reflection.

Fairy Flower Fun

These green-fingered girls are busy watering their pretty flowers. Can you spot the one that's different?

FAIRY FACT: The world's biggest flowers grow to be as tall as elephants!

Cute and Cuddly

It's a furry, feathery, fluffy pet show!
Fill the showground with fairies
and their animal friends.

Woof!

Make these "Best in Show" ribbons fairy-tastic with rainbow colors.

Best in Show

And the winner is ...

Meow

Woof!

Beside the Seaside

Fairies love to relax on the beach.
Add as many as you like with your stickers,
and don't forget their seaside friends!

Fairy Snacks!

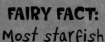

FAIRY FACT:
Most starfish
have 5 arms,
but some have as
many as 50!

Even mermaids have wings in Fairy Land!
Make this one look magical
by coloring her in.

Super Stars

This is a sandcastle fit
for a superstar fairy!
How many star shapes can
you spot in the picture?
Don't forget this one!

Home Sweet Fairy Home!

Which one of these lucky fairies lives in Toffee Apple Cottage?
Follow each one through the maze to find out.

Toffee Apple Cottage

welcome

Welcome to Toadstool Lane!

There's not mush-room in there!

Come on in!

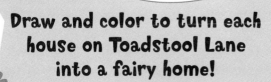

Draw and color to turn each house on Toadstool Lane into a fairy home!

FAIRY FACT:
A Falabella is
a miniature horse
the size
of a big dog!

Kitchen Treats

These clever cooks have been whipping up some sweet treats in the kitchen. Join the sprinkles to find out what each fairy has made.

Can you spot each fairy's favorite fruit?
Draw lines to match them up!

Pixie Picnic

Fairy picnics are flutterific fun, especially if you invite pixies along!

Slurp!!

Spot each of these things on the picnic rug above.
Stick a star when you find each one.

Sports Day Stars

On your marks, get set... go, fairies!
Add as many running, jumping, and
racing fairies as you can.

Hurry up,
slow poke.

FINISH

Draw some fabulously
fluffy pompoms for these
fairy cheerleaders.

Twirl and Hop!

Fairy ballerinas love to spin and twirl!
Can you match each dancer to her shadow?

Fill in the missing numbers to finish off these fairy hopscotch grids.

Fairy Fact or Fib?

The Fairy Land pool is shaped like a flower—that's a fact!

**Which of these are facts and which are fairy fibs?
Check off the right box.**

The fairy on the diving board has a stripy swimsuit.   TRUE ☐ FALSE ☐

. The fairy with the groovy goggles has pink hair.   TRUE ☐ FALSE ☐

. The blonde-haired fairy has a blue flower in her hair.   TRUE ☐ FALSE ☐

Nice and Icy!

The tastiest place in Fairy Land is Minty's ice cream parlor! Make the shop busy with hungry fairy customers.

FAIRY FACT:
It takes about 50 licks to polish off a single-scoop ice cream cone!

Color the cones
to make each giant
ice cream a different
flavor.

Arty Smarty

I'm a doodle bug!

What a pretty mess!
Join the dots to see
what these arty fairies
are painting.

Super Doodles

Find out which masterpiece belongs to each fairy, then help to finish each picture.

Seeing Spots

Help draw on the missing spots so each ladybug has the same number on both wings.

Unicorn Derby

Follow the lines to find out which unicorn will be first to cross the finish line.

1st

Blowing Bubbles

Who has blown the most fairy bubbles—
Daisy, Bluebell or Poppy? Count each
color to find out.

Daisy

Bluebell

Poppy

Animal Magic

Even fairies have fluff-tastic animal friends!
Follow the sparkly trails to
find out who each pet belongs to.

FAIRY FACT:
A newborn
kitten weighs
about the same
as a cupcake!

Happy

Pop!

Birthday parties are sparkle-tast celebrations in Fairy Land! Fill the floor with dancing party guests.

Color each birthday present with bright gift-wrapping designs.

Winter Wonderland

These fairies are having "snow" much fun!

Use your favorite shades to color them in.

Whoosh!

Fairy Friends

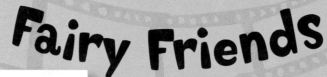

♥ Powder Puff

♥ Lottie Pop

♥ Dewdrop

♥ Little Lou

Rosy ♥

Look at these fairy photo-booth snapshots to work out which of these facts are true, and which are false. Check off the right box.

Dewdrop has pink hair.　　　　　　　　　　　TRUE ☐ FALSE ☐

. Lottie Pop has dotty wings.　　　　　　　　TRUE ☐ FALSE ☐

. Little Lou is wearing a tiara.　　　　　　　TRUE ☐ FALSE ☐

. Rosy has curly hair and lots of freckles.　　TRUE ☐ FALSE ☐

Showtime!

Lights, cameras, action!
Let's see who's got the Fairy Factor ...
Add singers, dancers, acrobats, and clowns to compete
on stage, and an audience to watch them perform.

Roller Fairies

Spot and circle 5 differences between these
skate-tastic pictures.

Love Hearts

How many heart shapes can you find in this pretty fairy bedroom?

Sleepover Party

Make this sleepover something special by adding fairies snoozing, bouncing, and midnight-feasting!

Pillow fight!

I love popcorn.

Draw fancy patterns to decorate these sleeping bags.

Fairies Rock!

The Sparkle Girls are Fairy Land's most pop-tastic band. Can you match each musical member to her popstar shadow?

Twin-tastic

Fairy twins Twinkledee and Twinkledum love to
snuggle up and watch Saturday night TV!
Follow the trails to find out each twin's favorite show.

♪ *The
Fairy
Factor* ♫

Sunflower
Street

Story
time!

These twins are bonkers about books!
Can you spot 5 differences between them?

Twilight Twinkles

It's the end of another magical day in Fairy Land.
Add more fairy friends to sparkle in the starlight.

Princess Picnic Party

You're invited to a princess tea party! Fill this pretty picture with more sandwiches, cakes, and drinks.

Use your stickers to give each teddy bear a tiara!

Princess tip: A princess is kind to animals as well as people!

Choosing Shoes

Which line leads Princess Polly to her missing shoe?

Puzzling Pile

Draw lines to match the pairs of princess shoes and boots.

Now find and circle four princess purses.

Princess Pumps

Give these shoes some princess sparkle by adding sequins and jewels.

Party Princess

Every princess loves to spin, twirl, and dance with her friends. But this ballroom is bare! Fill it up with decorations and princess guests.

Princess tip: A princess is friendly and welcoming!

Princess Playtime

Can you help Princess Rose
find her way through
the maze to her friends
in the middle?

Flutter-by Butterfly

Find and circle five differences between these utterly fluttery pictures.

Sparkly Shadows

Princesses come in all shapes and sizes. Some are tall and some are short. Match each princess to her shadow.

A   B   C   D

1   2   3   4

Palace Kitchen

These sweet-toothed princesses love to help out in the kitchen. Add cupcakes and treats of your own!

Decorate the cakes!

Princess tip: Princesses gladly help others!

Secret Shoppers

There are five princesses in this picture.
Can you find and circle them all?

Fashion Favorites

Princesses love matching accessories!
Color in these shoes to match these bags.

One of these tiaras is not like the rest. Can you spot the odd one out?

A   B   C   D

Flower Fair

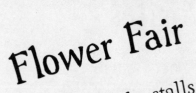

Add more flowers to the stalls and more princesses enjoying the palace garden flower show.

Color these roses in your favorite colors.

Count the daisies.

Princess tip: A princess loves pretty flowers!

Princess Painting

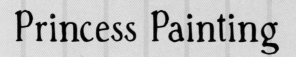

Are you ready to draw
Princess Daisy's portrait?
Make her as pretty as you can!

Picture Perfect

What a princess-perfect picture! Connect the dots to find out what this arty princess is painting.

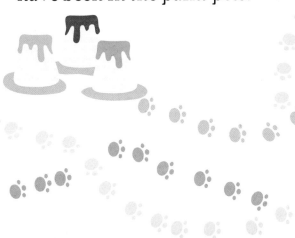

Painted Paws

Uh-oh! Which pet's paws have been in the paint pots?

A

B

C

Princess Sleepover

It's time for a princess slumber party!
Add more princesses and toys for them to play with.

Princess tip: A princess likes to have fun with her friends!

Princess Brunch

There are five differences between these two pictures. Can you find them all?

Princess Puzzle

Help this princess complete the puzzle. Find and circle the last jigsaw piece.

Rainy Day Fun

It's raining outside, so the princesses are playing hide-and-seek! Can you find three princesses hiding?

Missing Jewelry

Uh-oh! The princesses have been playing dressing up and have lost the royal jewels!

Find and circle:
1 diamond necklace
2 sapphire bracelets
3 ruby rings

Princess tip: Princesses love dressing up!

How many tiaras can you count?

How many bags can you count?

Use your stickers to add
more gems and jewels!

Pretty Ponies

Color in the saddles,
reins, and leg warmers.
Then dress the ponies up
in jewels, ribbons, and tiaras!

Pony Path

Which trail of hoofprints leads
Princess Poppy to the royal stables?

Pony Pairing

Only one of these shadows matches this pony
exactly. Circle the matching shadow.

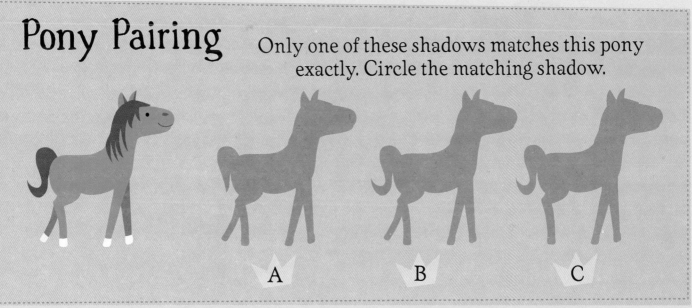

A   B   C

Princess Playground

Yippee, it's playtime! Fill the playground with swinging, skipping, and scooting princesses.

Princess tip: A real princess plays happily with others!

Princess Diary

What has Princess Daisy
drawn in her diary?
Connect the dots to find out!

33

35   1

34

32   2

31

30   5

29   4   6

28   7

27   26   3

25   10

22   9

21   18   17   14   8

Now color
the picture.   16   15   12   11

24   23

20   19

Make this your very own princess diary page.
Draw a pretty picture of yourself dressed as a princess.

Write your
name here.

Circle the animal
you like the best.

Ballerina Princess

Look at these pretty princesses leaping and twirling!
Fill this ballet classroom with more ballerina
princesses learning to dance.

Princess tip: A true princess always tries her best!

Princess Packing

Sun, sand, and sea! Princess Lily is going on a beach vacation.
Circle five things to pack, then draw them in the suitcase.

Don't forget to add shoes and tiaras, too!

Princess Pairs

Which sun hat
matches this one exactly?

A

B

C

Jet-setting Princess

There are five differences between these jet-setting princess pictures.
Can you find them all?

Fluttering Friends

Princesses love beautiful butterflies!
Fill the palace gardens with more princesses
and their fluttering friends.

How many butterflies can you count?

How many bunnies can you count?

How many unicorns can you count?

Princess tip: A princess never moans or complains!

Banquets and Balls

These princesses love dressing up
for royal banquets and balls!
Color their dresses and shoes
in your favorite colors.

Splish Splash!

The princesses are learning how to swim!
Use your stickers to give them armbands and inner tubes.

Add more princess
swimmers in the pool.

Princess tip: Princesses like to learn new things!

Playful Puppies

Oops! Princess Lola has forgotten
to wipe her puppy's paws!
Follow the trail of muddy
paw prints to find out
where he is hiding.

Puppies in the Park

There are five differences between these two pictures.
Can you find them all?

Puppy Pairing
Only one of these shadows matches this puppy exactly. Circle the matching shadow.

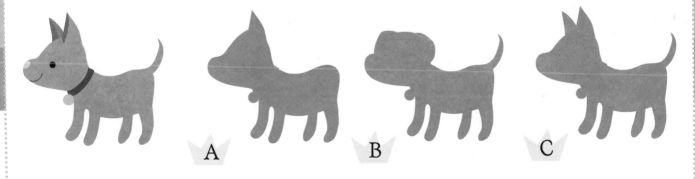

A   B   C

Princess Library

Princesses love reading books—especially fairy tales!
Fill the room with more books for these princesses to read.

Princess tip: Princesses enjoy reading and writing!

Princess School

Welcome to Princess School, where young princesses from far and wide are taught! Connect the dots to find out what this class is learning today.

Classroom Line

Which princess has brought her pet in for show-and-tell?

A B C D

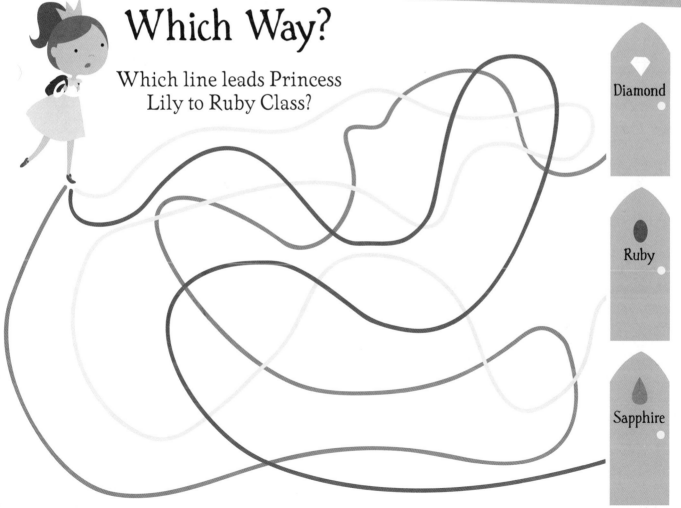

Which Way?

Which line leads Princess Lily to Ruby Class?

Diamond

Ruby

Sapphire

Princess Ponies

Fill these royal stables with
prize ponies and their proud owners!

Princess tip: Princesses enjoy taking care of animals!

Answers

Which little kitten has unraveled the knitting?

Match each kitten with its bed.

Can you find eight differences between these two pictures?

How many mattresses does the princess have on her bed?

 15

Princess Poppy is late for the ball! Which route will take her to her carriage and horses?

Princess Isabella must kiss the frog prince by the fountain to turn it into a handsome prince.

Draw a circle around each thing Hattie needs to go horseback riding.

Penny's pony doesn't like the water jumps! Can you show Penny a way through the show jumping course that avoids all the water jumps?

Spot five differences between these two show jumping horses.

Draw lines to match each poodle to its shadow.

Help the puppy find his way home through the maze.

Circle all the things that need to packed into the picnic basket.

Can you find the matching pair?

Can you find three differences between these twins?

Help this fairy through the forest to find her friend.

How many fairies have a wand with a star on? 2

Which two of these fairies have the same pattern on their wings?

Answers

Draw lines to match the pretty pairs.

Spot 5 differences.

Can you spot the one that's different?

There are 6 wands.

There are 14 star shapes in this sandcastle picture.

This fairy lives in Toffee Apple Cottage.

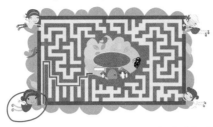

Draw lines between each fairy and her matching fruit.

Spot each of these things on the picnic rug above.

Can you match each dancer to her shadow?

Fairy Fact or Fib?
1. FALSE
2. TRUE
3. FALSE

This unicorn made it first past the finish line.

Daisy has blown 8 bubbles. She has blown the most.

Fairy Friends
1. FALSE
2. TRUE
3. FALSE
4. TRUE

Spot 5 differences.

There are 10 heart shapes in this pretty fairy bedroom.

Can you match each musical member to her popstar shadow?

Can you spot 5 differences between the twins?

Answers

Choosing Shoes
The pink line leads Princess Polly to her missing shoe.

Spot and circle four princess handbags.

Help Princess Rose find her way through the maze.

Spot and circle five differences.

Sparkly Shadows
A2, B3, C1, D4

Find and circle five princesses.

Fashion Favorites
Tiara C is the odd one out.

Connect the dots to find out what this arty princess is painting.

Painted Paws
Pet A's paws have been in the paint pots.

Can you spot five differences?

Princess Puzzle
Piece A is the last jigsaw piece.

Can you find three princesses hiding?

How many tiaras and bags can you count?

There are 9 tiaras and 4 bags.

Pony Path
The trail of yellow hoof prints leads Princess Poppy to the royal stables.

Pony Pairing
Shadow B matches the pony exactly.

Connect the dots.

Princess Pairs
A matches the sun hat exactly.

Can you spot five differences?

Fluttering Friends
There are 10 butterflies, 3 bunnies, and 3 unicorns.

Can you spot five differences?

Puppy Pairing
Shadow C matches the puppy exactly.

Connect the dots to find out what this class is learning today.

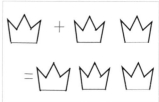

Classroom Queue
Princess A has brought her pet in for show-and-tell.

Which Way?
The blue line leads Princess Lily to Ruby class.